Nursery Rhymes
mother never read you

for grown-ups and precocious kids

WRITTEN AND ILLUSTRATED BY
GARRICK TREMAIN

Published by Craig Printing Company Limited,
122 Yarrow Street, PO Box 99, Invercargill 9840, New Zealand.

© 2005 Garrick Tremain

ISBN 0-908629-62-1

First impression 2005
Second 2006, Third 2008, Fourth 2009

Printed by Craig Printing Company Limited,
122 Yarrow Street, PO Box 99, Invercargill 9840, New Zealand.
Email: sales@craigprint.co.nz   Website: www.craigprint.co.nz
119227

the Contents

Noah got a text from God
"Better build a boat!
The bloody weather's packing up;
it's either drown or float!"

So Noah built a sailing ship
from sticks and bits of bark;
put a gangway to the deck
and called it Noah's Ark.

Then he faxed the animals,
"Wanna save your life?
Sailing time is half past three;
be here with your wife!"

And so they congregated,
they knew he didn't jest;
arriving in long columns
from north, south, east and west.

Ten seconds from departure
an Asian porcupine
said, "Hey, there are no pussy cats!
And not much that's canine!"

"That's their tough luck," said Noah,
"we simply cannot wait;
they were told, like everyone,
on no account be late!"

As they cast off from shore
two tiny little frogs
cried, "It's okay! Here they come!
It's raining cats and dogs!"

Percy

Percy was a penguin,
only twelve months old,
who lived down in Antarctica
but couldn't stand the cold.

He hated snow and blizzards
and waddling 'round on ice;
he said he felt brass monkeyish
which wasn't very nice.

He'd rocket down a snowfield,
sliding on his gut,
and if he came down backwards
would hold his bottom shut.

Otherwise he'd fill with snow
abdominal amounts,
until the very force of it
would turn him inside out.

Then Percy would retire to bed
sighing, "Woe is me!"
and read his travel brochures
on Tahiti and Fiji.

Jack

A tortoise known as Jack
lugged his house upon his back,
a feat which made poor Jack a trifle slow;
those who tote their shells
never need motels,
they have their digs no matter where they go.

He rued the day he'd seen
'House and Garden' magazine,
and being trendy thought that he'd update;
he got the builders in
who made a frightful din,
as builders do when asked to renovate.

Jack was tickled pink
with bath and kitchen sink,
he even had new internet connection;
the parquet wooden floor
was just as he'd hoped for,
and showed his Persian rug off to perfection.

Now the house Jack owns is
right up with the Jones's,
fitted out with all the latest gear...
the best that he could get,
he has just one regret,
the indoor loo was not a good idea.

Brian was a garden snail
who left a shiny, sticky trail
as he slid along dragging his behind;
ravenous snail-eaters
would follow it for metres,
it made our Brian an easy chap to find.

Brian's wife was Flossy,
rather butch and bossy,
at night she'd follow it the other way
to see where Brian had been;
it led her to Irene,
so Flossy knew that Brian wasn't gay.

But Brian couldn't win,
his trail had dobbed him in,
he admitted extra-marital offences;
if you're that way inclined
keep poor Brian in mind...
hide your tracks or face the consequences.

Brian

the
Mouse

The biggest nuisance in a house
is the smallest occupant, a mouse,
every goddamned thing he chews
and dots the shelves with tiny poos.

We've got one, precious little chap,
at least he would be in a trap,
but from the trap the cheese he'll scoff
without the darn thing going off.

One thing I really wish is that
we had a ghastly bloody cat
to disembowel him with a claw
and smear his giblets 'round the floor.

I blocked his hole up, just for spite,
jammed it up with gum real tight,
it's hardly cramped his style one bit
but he walks peculiar and can't sit.

Herbert
the
Hedgehog

Herbert was a hedgehog,
a prickly little chappy,
not just depressed but really,
really quite unhappy.

He'd sit about and mope and moan
and weep enormous puddles,
because his rotten mummy
never gave him cuddles.

Mother said, "Now really, dear,
I'm such a loving mummy;
don't I turn you upside down
and rub you on the tummy?"

I may not give you cuddles,
that we cannot fix,
no one cuddles hedgehogs;
they're such a bunch of pricks.

Mary had a Little Lamb

Mary had a little lamb,
a very tiny portion,
and thought the price she paid for it
nothing but extortion.

And Mary found the little lamb
tough as old boot leather,
suspecting they had served her up
old merino wether.

What was worse, the wretched dish
upset her tummy so,
every time she coughed or sneezed
she was sure to go.

Another time she tried the pork
and asked for apple sauce,
the waiter brought her horseradish
which burned her tongue of course.

The day she ordered chicken breast
the chef forgot to pluck it,
and Mary spent the next three days
sitting on a bucket.

She bought a book of recipes
and now cooks what she wants,
Mary's had a gutsful
of fancy restaurants.

Little Tim

Little Tim found in the shed
three little kittens born to Fred,
the family cat that they'd all thought
a cat of quite the other sort.

"Mummy! Mummy! Come and see!"
cried excited Timothy,
"Three little kittens warm and snug
curled up together on Fred's rug!"

"Goodness gracious," Mummy said,
"such a clever mother, Fred!"
Tim couldn't wait to tell his Dad
of the dear wee kittens Fred had had.

"I think," said Dad to Little Tim,
"we ought to take them for a swim,"
and so they did that very thing …
with a brick, in a sack, tied up with string.

Old Mother Hubbard

Old Mother Hubbard
went to the cupboard
to fetch her poor doggie a bone.

When she got there
the cupboard was bare,
she'd forgotten, silly old crone.

"I want bloody fed!"
her wee doggie said
and called her a miserly whore.

To the back fence she led him
and grinned as she fed him
to the Doberman Pinscher next door.

Malcolm

Malcolm was a housefly,
small but rather scary,
with eyes like plates of caviare
and legs all black and hairy.

He'd buzz around the living room
on wee transparent wings,
passing through some flyspray,
then headlong into things.

Feeling less than well he'd crash
onto the windowsill,
do some calisthenics
then finally lie still.

All said and done, it seems to me,
there's not much to be said
for doing kamikaze tricks
and finishing up dead.

To be reincarnated
is something I would welcome...
but hope that I can guarantee
I don't come back as Malcolm.

Buttercup

A little pig called Buttercup
suspected she was growing up
when she noticed on her tummy
lots of buttons just like Mummy.

"Good Grief!" she cried, "They're in two rows,
but what they're for God only knows!
Is this what's known as puberty?
Or is there something wrong with me?"

Her Mummy said, "Don't be alarmed,
they're just part of our female charm;
you may well find, when you get old,
you'll be a PlayPig centerfold."

Daddy Pig was thrilled to bits,
his girl had grown thirteen tits;
he claimed they were a gift from God,
but thought thirteen was rather odd.

He'd not before seen such a set
and took her off to see the vet,
who found the reason, pure and simple,
the thirteenth one was just a pimple.

Tilly, a small tadpole,
in a garden pond,
lived on insect larvae,
of which tadpoles are fond.

Concerned one day, Tilly said,
"There's something very strange,
peculiar things are happening,
I'm undergoing change.
Suddenly I have an urge
to climb out of the water,
my body's getting slimmer,
my tail's becoming shorter.
And I'm turning greener,
not nearly quite so black,
feet are growing on my bum,
trailing out the back."

Then flexing all her brand new limbs
she climbed up on a log:
as if a prince had kissed her
she turned into a frog.

"I'm getting old!" squealed Tilly,
and had a little cry.
"Don't be silly, you're not old,"
said a dragonfly.

As is the way with dragonflies,
he made a little joke,
"You'll find you're never truly old,
until the day you croak!"

Tilly

a Newborn Unicorn

A white unicorn
produced her firstborn,
a tiny horse hairless and pink;
a beautiful colt
without blemish or fault
which mums, as you know, always think.

As she gazed in the cot
she said, "What he's got
is intelligence, good looks and charm",
but suddenly saw
what she'd not seen before
which caused her to cry in alarm.

"Come here, Papa!
this is really bizarre!
It's only two weeks he's been born!
Try not to wake 'im,
unless I'm mistaken,
I think he's just got his first horn!"

Charlie was a sand crab
who lived on rotting kippers
he found along the shoreline
and tore up with his nippers.

"Variety," said Charlie,
"would be good for my diet,
if I could find some non-seafood
I'd be real keen to try it."

Just as Charlie thought his dream
was really out of reach,
a partly eaten sandwich
dropped onto the beach.

Charlie
Crab

"Yum yum," he said "I'm into this,
an unexpected treat,"
but found out that the sandwich
was made of tinned crab meat.

"Tempted though I am," said Charles,
"I'll eat this at my peril,
I'd know that odour anywhere,
Good Lord... it's Aunty Beryl!"

Olive

Olive was an Orpington
who wished she'd been hard wired,
for every day just after lunch
she got extremely tired.

When really low on energy
she'd spit upon her comb,
and jam it in those three-point plugs
you have around the home.

After thirty minutes
she'd be recharged again;
it's just a thing you have to do
if you're a battery hen.

An aphid known as Alfred
lived on a crimson rose
with such a lovely fragrance
folk would stick their nose
in amongst the petals
to sniff the scented cup,
until one day a lady
sniffed poor Alfred up.

Alfred was unhappy
with his newfound lot,
a dark and drafty passage
his legs tied up with snot;
he used his tiny fingers
to irritate her snout,
hoping in reaction
she might just sneeze him out.

His hostess wasn't ticklish
life became a bore,
until the lady went to bed...
Jeepers! Could she snore!
"I can't sleep!" wailed Alfred,
"with this frightful din!
I'll get some sleep tomorrow...
unless herself sleeps in."

Aphid

the Rat and the Mole

Desmond was a biker rat,
tattoos, patches, chains and that,
sinister, gnarly,
riding a Harley,
a war helmet as a crash hat.

His medal, a Nazi swastika,
his tipple, Jack Daniels liquor,
he'd swig from the bottle
then open the throttle
convinced that he went a lot quicker.

His lady, the trendy Ma-ryka,
was the envy of many a biker,
adorning his pillion,
dark shades and Brazilian...
and Desmond pretended to like her.

Wherever he rode Desmond took her
and other bike rats all mistook her
for the love of his life
or maybe his wife
and hailed her a really good-looker

Said Desmond, feigning surprise
"She's not a good-looker, you guys,
no way can she be,
Ma-ryka can't see...
a biker's mole doesn't have eyes!"

a Talented Parrot

A talented parrot
with considerable merit
could imitate all that he heard,
from church bells to thunder
even Stevie would wonder
such noises could come from a bird.

He had perfect pitch
and could suddenly switch
from telephones ringing and sing
an opening stanza
by Mario Lanza
to Presley, Caruso or Sting.

Then he'd go on
and do Elton John,
Bob Dylan, Ray Charles, Peggy Lee.
His fans said, "Good Lord!
You have to record!
You'll be famous as famous can be!"

He said, "Damn the risk!
I shall cut a disk!"
but the whole thing went straight to his head.
While doing a jig
he tripped on a twig
and fell down and slipped one instead.

the Brothers Bot

(A bot fly of course is
a fly that bugs horses
– something not everyone knows –
by laying its eggs
on their bellies and legs
so now that you know that, here goes...)

A tiny bot egg
on a draught horse's leg
was yelling out things to his brother,
'cause the little bot egg
was on a front leg
and his brother was back on another.

To be perfectly blunt
it was best up the front
'cause the horse was a wonderful doer,
and the one at the rear
just couldn't hear
'cause his ear was full of manure.

Colin was a cockerel
and just like lots of men,
he'd wink an eye and throw a leg
at any passing hen.
But when a really ugly one
came into the yard,
he'd say, "I think I'll have a spell,
it isn't really hard
to show a little self control,
I think you will agree,
when there's forty-five of them
and only one of me.
If one's not selective
when one's throwing legs,
one gets a reputation
and an awful lot of eggs."

Colin the Cockerel

the Warthog

A very punctual warthog
who lived in mud and slime,
had one redeeming feature...
arriving right on time.

He wore a plastic wristwatch
just above his hoof,
which would have been quite useless
had it not been waterproof.

Every time he wound it up
he'd cry, "Well, goodness me,
is that the time already?
It's twenty-five to three!

"I have a hair appointment,
simply gotta rush!"
making farting noises
as he galloped through the slush.

Straight into a crocodile
he didn't know was there;
now he's called the late warthog
which really isn't fair!

Larks
on the
Ark

On the Ark, two animals
who loved a belly laugh
were Hugh the hippopotamus
and Gerald the giraffe.

The hyena p'raps was keener
on chortling and guffawing,
but didn't play the silly tricks
the others found so boring.

While the rest sat on the deck
spotting fish and whales,
these self-appointed comics
tied reef knots in their tails.

"This is great," giggled Hugh,
"the wild seafaring life,"
but wished Noah hadn't said
he'd had to bring his wife.

They wolf-whistled the peacock
and soon had him confessing
his penchant for outrageous gear
and clandestine cross-dressing.

"Watch me, Hugh!" said Gerald,
"Here's a likely jape!"
and smearing lipstick on his bum
cried, "I'm the Barbary Ape!"

When the dance band started up
they asked the fox to trot,
at the bar they shouted, "Leopard!
Would you like a spot?"

They asked the owl if he was wise
as every comic does,
and told the honeybee he gave
the two of them a buzz.

They asked the female starfish
what made her such a star,
but couldn't hear her answer
as they went, "Oh, ha ha ha!"

They'd compliment the pandas
on their fluffy slippers,
and ask the blushing lobster,
"How's the wife and nippers?"

Next they tried sea burial,
"Awfully sad," they joked,
dispatching cane toad to the deep
because they said he'd croaked.

When Noah said, "Go easy, boys!
Your constant pranking niggles!"
They looked forlorn but then dissolved
in fits of helpless giggles.

They thought this little reprimand
a futile thing indeed...
only saw the funny side
and laughed until they peed.

As they roared in raucous mirth
and unrepentant glee,
they slipped in their own puddles
and fell into the sea.

Their unforeseen departure
Brought universal smiles,
the only tears shed, of course...
were from the crocodiles.

the Mermaid

An apprentice fishmonger
had an erotic hunger
and bouts of sensual delirium.
His particular fancy
was a mermaid called Nancy
he kept in a plastic aquarium.

Besotted, his flounder,
Would hover around her,
she was a true gift from the Gods.
Somewhere in the story
up popped his John Dory
and he struggled to cope with his cods.

Runnymede

A golden stag called Runnymede
was brave and strong and blessed with speed.

The ruler of the forest glen,
he feared no foes, not even men.

The latter fact is why, no doubt,
what brains he had got blown out.

Bert the Hippo

Bert the hippo suffered stress,
his wife said, "Bert, you're such a mess!
It's plain to me, you would be
better off if you drank less!"

Though he didn't flinch or blink
or care much what his wife should think,
she got her way, he joined AA
who told him he must never drink.

Persuaded drinking is a curse,
and only makes your problems worse,
we are told that waterholes
he now approaches in reverse.

He backs right in, up to his hips,
his backside taking tiny sips,
and thus can claim, no fear, no blame,
that ne'er a drop has passed his lips.

the Moth

The household moth's a funny mite,
sleeps all day and then at night,
emerges from the gloomy attic
feeling very aerobatic,
quickly flexing all his wings
then blindly flying into things;
he thinks it's fun so what the heck,
life is short and so's his neck.

It matters little what you've got,
forty or one-hundred watt,
he loops the loop and follows through
like kamikaze pilots do.
Such daring and determination,
he knows that Civil Aviation
cannot, on him, enforce their law,
they're all at home by half past four.

It does occur that maybe we
could harness all this energy,
fit him with a tiny hopper
to be a super phosphate dropper.
A hatchway in his underpants
could fertilise the indoor plants;
thus employed he'd be a blessing,
zooming to and fro topdressing.

Such nutrition in the air
on father might just grow some hair.

('Twould do nothing of the sort...
Never mind... 'twas just a thought.)

Phil

Phil, a white rhinoceros,
was something of a prude
who'd go as pink as rhubarb
at things he thought were rude.

"So much is disgusting!"
prudish Phil insisted,
just amazed that nudist clubs
and things like that existed.
"Ridiculous!" expounded Phil,
"Not my idea of fun!
Mingling with your naughty bits
jiggling in the sun!"

Browsing through the papers
he simply couldn't bear
advertisements for toilet rolls
and ladies' underwear.
When he came across them
he'd blush magenta rose,
and find them like his rampant horn...
rather on the nose.

the Family Cat

Our family cat
converts wee birds
to piles of feathers, guts and turds,
then spreads them round
upon the mat...
a lovely bloody thing, a cat!

William

William was an earthworm
who lived deep underground
in holes which, just like William,
are longer than they're round.

He had a little girlfriend,
a she-worm known as Betty,
as pale and slim and shapely
as newly boiled spaghetti.

"Hey Bet, you're such a stunner!"
said William with a giggle,
"You've got a super saddle
and such a fetching wiggle!"

He had a clever line of chat,
it bubbled out verbatim,
until a starling hearing him
pulled him up and ate 'im.

Freddy

Freddy was a frog
basking on a log,
with a yen for something really yummy;
every time a fly
came a-buzzing by,
ZAP! it disappeared in Freddy's tummy.

He felt rather smart
dining a la carte,
zapping passing fastfood was the caper;
it is a froggy trick,
a tongue so long and quick
and every bit as sticky as fly paper.

Things went along okay
till a hornet came his way
and Freddy, in a flash, shot out his tongue...
then cried, "Bugger me!
That must've been a bee!
Unless I am mistook I have been stung!"

Tears came to his eyes,
his tongue grew twice its size
swelling to a painful, purple bubble;
he remembered he'd been told
when just a wee tadpole,
"Your tongue, young man, will get you into trouble!"

Jock McScratch

A Scottish flea called Jock McScratch
had made a homely little patch,
burrowed out a cosy warren
deep in Sam McWhirter's sporran,
and from the sporran Jock would launch
lighting raids upon Sam's paunch.

Jock with life was quite content
but 'round the bend Sam nearly went,
he'd itch and scratch and do his best
to corner Jock in kilt or vest;
for a Scotsman it's completely foreign
to publicly attack the sporran.

Sam at last could take no more
he slammed his sporran in the door,
then banged it hard between his knees
but still the itching didn't ease;
at last in frightful desperation
he planned a mighty conflagration.

It was indeed a desperate plan
with matches and a petrol can,
and with the petrol can held high
he shrieked, "You're finished, Jock, Och Aye!"
Emitting one last fearful cackle
he doused his kilt and wedding tackle.

He burned his sporran to the bone
and ever since Sam's lived alone.

Priscilla

Wee Priscilla
caterpillar
feeling so contrary;
didn't mind
her fat behind
but hated being hairy.

What girl does
enjoy the fuzz
that sprouts from head to heel;
Priscilla thought
removal ought
to lift her sex appeal.

She brought a tube
of sticky goob
to rub on every day;
the label said
that if she did
the hair would go away.

She understood
that baldness would
display her figure better;
but now she's bald
she feels the cold
and has to wear a sweater.

A tiny little batfly
whose Mum had called him Peter,
lived on the floors of gloomy caves
Eating bat excreta.

Such an unfulfilling life
rather sad and tragic,
there's not a lot to recommend
being coprophagic.

Peter
and
Beth

He had a little girlfriend,
the gorgeous batfly, Beth,
who found him handsome in the dark
but couldn't go his breath.

"It's worse than halitosis,"
she whispered in good grace,
"kiss me when and where you like
but please not on the face."

Cuthbert was a cobra
with a love of opera,
the other snakes all thought that he was dotty;
he ignored their jeers,
he at least had ears
and knew he sounded just like Pavarotti.

He thought it all a shame
'cause one day he'd have fame,
might even get his own show on the telly;
while they were eating snails
he practised all his scales,
not just the ones that ran along his belly.

One day it transpired
Cuthbert did get hired,
to sing Puccini
down at Covent Garden,
which the snakes poo-pooed,
they were so bloody rude
they didn't even say,
"We beg your pardon."

Cyril was a crocodile,
no one liked him much
because he dined on cattle beasts,
human beings and such;
the trouble was that Cyril
totally adored
pearl divers and fishermen
who'd fallen overboard.

He wanted folk to like him
and vowed to change his ways,
cutting back his diet
to jellyfish and crays;
he scavenged around tent sites
for bits of bread and damper,
ignoring passing servings
of holidaying camper,
who'd go as white as ghost gums,
immediately freeze,
arms held out like branches,
imitating trees,
or try to climb each other,
irrational with fear,
unaware he had abstained
for coming up a year.

Cyril

Occasionally Cyril
would think of what he'd missed,
but say, "Now come on, Cyril –
you really must desist!"
until December twenty-fifth
in North Australian heat,
he gobbled down a jackeroo
just as a Christmas treat.

C.G.S. Brown

Cedric Granville Spencer Brown
spent each day hung upside down,
it's how you spend each day if you're a bat;
so when he had to do
a little pee or poo
it ran into his eyes and filled his hat.

Cedric thought he might
defecate at night
when he flew, his head above his bottom;
when going through the day
he was always in the way
and every time he did a bit it got 'im.

At night he didn't get
as smelly or as wet,
which added quite a lot to Cedric's charms;
to make his life much better
and stop him getting wetter,
he started sleeping hanging by his arms.

Hanging by one's toes,
as every cave bat knows,
means one's in the road of one's behind;
now Cedric understands
had he occupied his hands
perhaps it would have stopped him going blind.

Praying Mantis

A wee praying mantis
(if you're wondering what that is
and think that it sounds a bit odd),
is a special insect
who shows great respect
and considerable faith in his God.

This one was Patrick,
a green Roman Catholic,
famous from Ireland to Spain;
a mover and shaker
with a line to his maker,
in droughts he could get it to rain.

One day, it appears,
he was muttering prayers
of redemption, goodwill and love;
his praying was heard
by God and a bird
and one of them swooped from above.

With one lightning crunch
Patrick was lunch,
we never saw Patrick again;
it's a God-given sport
so keep your prayers short,
perhaps even start with "Amen".

Lucy was a reindeer,
Lapland was her home;
went to school in Budapest,
Switzerland and Rome.
At a smart academy
in the South of France,
a vintner's daughter taught her
the finer points of dance.

"Not for me," said Lucy,
"a life of pulling sleighs;
I was born to titilate,
startle and amaze.
I'm not a beast of burden,
it's the dancer's life I choose;
I'm going to be a household name,
have ribbons on my shoes!'

Lucy

She proved to be a natural,
soon was all the rage;
people threw rose petals
as she sprang onto the stage.
She filled the Colosseum,
brought down the Albert Hall,
the toast of Munich bierfests,
she wowed them in Nepal.

She loved the adulation,
the money and the fame,
but suddenly it finished
as quickly as it came.
An Arabian promoter
introduced her in Algiers
as "Lucy the Lapp Dancer"
and she left the stage in tears.

Primrose

Primrose was a pretty pig,
a famous belly dancer;
whenever propositioned
"No, sorry," was the answer.

Her loving husband, Bernard,
a large white Berkshire boar,
was the bouncer and collected
the tickets at the door.

When tables full of rowdies
yelled, "Get yer gear off! Do!"
She might expose a little boob
but never more that two.

She travelled to Morocco
to dance in Marrakech
'cause Bernard said the Muslim chaps
liked their pound of flesh.

But she and Bernard had to leave
Morocco in disgrace;
she'd let her yashmak slip a bit
and shown them half her face.

on the Net

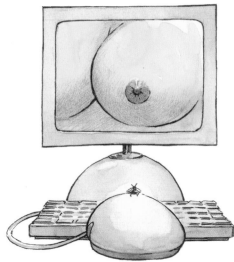

A busy little housefly
buzzed around the house,
into the computer room
and landed on the mouse.

He could've landed on one leg
but was a trifle thick;
he landed one leg at a time
which made a double click.

It took him to a chatroom
then porn, more soft than hard;
he couldn't access grubby stuff
without a credit card.

Indeed he was besotted
with the internet;
never had such fun before
and would have been there yet,
but kept on double clicking,
which really was unwise ...
brought up the spider's website
and that was his demise.

a Miner

A miner from down on the Arrow
took a dancehall tart home on his barrow,
but fitting a condom
proved quite beyond 'im,
so he used it to frost-proof his marrow.

A sporting old north country vicar
bought a racehorse for 25 nicker,
he saved a few pound
but very soon found
the dearer ones go a bit quicker.

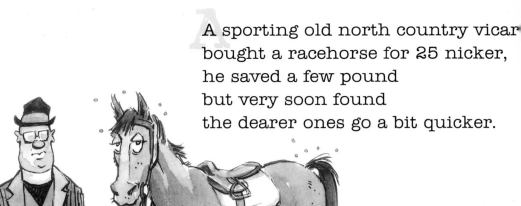

Haemophilia, a mouse from Dunedin
had a nose that just wouldn't stop bleedin'
so she slept with her head
hanging under her bed,
so it bled in the pot that she peed in.